Bible Curriculum

Grow in God's Word

New Testament

Grades 1–2

Dedication: With love and appreciation to the members of the Church of Christ in Breckenridge, Texas, where I grew up. A special thanks to Judy Dye for her help and advice.

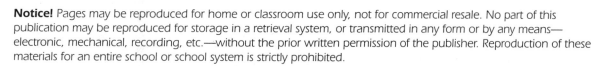

Written by Robin Wolfe
Illustrated by Marilynn Barr

Cover Design by Nehmen-Kodner

All rights reserved—Printed in the U.S.A.
Copyright © 2000 Shining Star Publications
A Division of Frank Schaffer Publications, Inc.
23740 Hawthorne Blvd., Torrance, CA 90505

Unless otherwise indicated, the New International Version of the Bible was used in preparing the activities in this book. Scripture taken from the HOLY BIBLE, NEW INTERNATIONAL VERSION. Copyright © 1973, 1978, 1984 International Bible Society. Used by permission of Zondervan Bible Publishers.

Table of Contents

Introduction

Children love to hear their favorite Bible stories over and over, but how many know where these stories occur on a time line of Bible history and why they are found in particular books of the Bible?

This book is a perfect resource for teachers and parents to use to help young children learn the history and order of the New Testament in a fun and exciting way. This knowledge will enable the children to better understand the scope and sequence of the Bible, its contents, and where to find particular stories they know. Although it is set up nicely for Sunday school and other Christian school teachers, many parents will want to use this book to extend Bible learning in their own homes.

The book contains mini-units for each of the 27 books of the New Testament. Some of the books have been combined into one mini-unit. Each mini-unit follows the same specified format and includes directions for beginning class, introducing the lesson, presenting the lesson, and concluding the lesson. Prayers, memory verses, flash cards, activity pages, and assignments are all part of each mini-unit. Be sure to discuss each component in the mini-units with the children to ensure understanding and relativity. The activity pages contained in the mini-units enable the children to learn some of the stories contained in a particular New Testament book and help the children better understand their place on the Biblical time line. (In some cases, you will need to read the stories featured on the activity pages before the children can complete the activities.)

Children will enjoy making puppets, drawing, acting out stories, and much more as they learn all about the New Testament and God's Word. (An answer key for the activity pages can be found on page 80.) As they complete the activities in this book, the children will also be practicing such valuable skills as reading, critical thinking, visual discrimination, and sequencing. Be sure to guide the children through each activity, providing the necessary help, encouragement, and explanations of directions or Biblical content. (You may want the children to store their activity pages and other components of this book in a special folder.)

Some of the objectives of this book for the children are as follows:

- to attend class and bring a Bible
- to become a member of the "Bible Story Club" (see page 71)
- to learn all of the books of the New Testament in order
- to learn that the name of each book gives a clue to what it is about
- to learn Bible stories from the New Testament
- to learn how to read a time line of the events in the New Testament
- to learn how each book of the New Testament fits on the time line
- to memorize a Bible verse for each mini-unit

You will be amazed at the wealth of information the children will receive as they complete the units in this book. To celebrate their learning, you might consider having an end-of-book party. The children can put on a program to show all that they have learned about the New Testament using the flash cards, charts, time line, and memory verses.

SS2000

Components of the Book

In addition to the mini-units, this book contains these components:

Bible Story Club Rules and Objectives
(page 71) Post a copy of these rules and objectives on a wall or bulletin board. Introduce them during the first lesson. Tell the children that each child can be a member of the club by promising to obey the club rules. (Let the children choose a club handshake or password.)

Attendance Chart
(page 72) Give each child a copy of this chart, and let the children color them. Mount them on colored paper. These may be posted on a wall or bulletin board. The children can add stickers or stars each week. Give one sticker for attendance and one sticker for bringing a Bible to class. (If stickers are not available, the children may color in the squares instead.)

New Testament Songs
(page 73) Each song teaches the books of the New Testament in order. Sing one of them with the children during each mini-unit introduction. As you sing it, point to each book of the New Testament on the chart from the back of the book. By doing this every time, the children will be able to memorize the books of the New Testament in order.

Bible Story Songs
(pages 74–75) A song pertaining to each mini-unit is provided on these pages. The songs are easy to learn because they are written to the tunes of familiar children's songs.

Time Line of the New Testament
(pages 76–77) Before the first class meeting, make a copy of the time line for each child. Then color the pictures on your copy. Mount and laminate it, if possible. Give each child a copy. Help the children tape the edges of their two pages together correctly to form the complete time line. The children should refer to this during each lesson. Keep these in the classroom for use

each time (or let the children keep them in their folders). There are two ways the children can use their time lines. Option 1: Each week, have the children color the pictures that apply only to that particular mini-unit. This will keep them focused and will help them learn how to use a time line. Option 2: Each week as the children come in, have them color the pictures from the previous week's lesson as a review before class begins.

Award
(page 78) Give a copy to each child upon completion of this book. Throughout the book, be generous with rewards, and be sure to praise the children over and over for their hard work. Candy, gum, and stickers make nice rewards.

"The 12 Apostles" Chart
(page 79) This chart is a great way to help the children learn about the 12 special men (and the one added later) that Jesus chose to help Him do His Father's work on earth. Give each child a copy to keep in his or her folder. It can be used many times throughout the book.

Flash Cards
In the back of the book, you will find 30 flash cards. Children learn by repetition. Use these cards over and over as a wonderful way to enhance the learning and understanding of the Bible's order, content, and other important information. Complete instructions of how and when to use the flash cards are included in each mini-unit.

"Books of the New Testament" Chart
In the back of the book, you will find a chart of the books of the New Testament. This is a wonderful reference tool for the children, so feel free to make each child a copy for his or her folder. Display your copy in a prominent place.

Unit 1 . . . . . . Matthew & Mark

BUSINESS

 ### Welcome

Tell the children that they are invited to be in the Bible Story Club. Read and explain the rules of the club (page 71). Have a "ceremony" in which each child promises to obey the rules. Then tell the children that they are now inducted into the club. Ask the children if they would like to have a secret handshake or password. Give them an award or ribbon that says "Bible Story Club."

 ### Attendance Charts

Give each child a copy of the attendance chart on page 72. Give each child one sticker for attendance and one for bringing a Bible. Or, instead of stickers, they can color in the squares. Put the attendance charts up on a wall or bulletin board.

 ### Prayer Requests and Prayer

At this time, take prayer requests from the children. Honor these and then say a class prayer to begin the lesson.

LESSON

 ### Lesson Introduction

Sing one of the songs on page 73. Using the chart in the back of the book, point to each book of the New Testament as you sing. Do this at the beginning of every class, as children learn by repetition. Tell the children that there is one theme throughout the Bible. (Show flash card 1.) It is important to stress this throughout the course of this book to give the children the overall message of the Bible. Also discuss flash cards 2–4 at this time.

 ### Lesson

Show the children the books of Matthew and Mark in the Bible. Tell the children that we can remember what each book of the Bible is about by its title. Matthew and Mark are two of the four gospels. Explain to the children that *gospel* means "good news." All four gospels tell the same story of the life of Jesus, each in its own way. (Show flash card 5.)

Lesson continued

Matthew—This is the first book of the New Testament. It was written by one of the apostles, a tax collector named Matthew. Read how Jesus called Matthew to be an apostle in Matthew 9:9–13. The book of Matthew tells the story of Jesus: His birth, baptism, teachings, miracles, and parables. It ends with the account of His death, burial, and resurrection.

Mark—This gospel was written by Mark, sometimes called John Mark. He was not an apostle, but he was a friend of Peter and Paul. (Acts 12:11–14; 2 Timothy 4:11) The book of Mark is a fast-moving account of the life of Jesus.

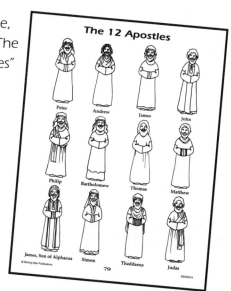

At this time, go over "The 12 Apostles" chart on page 79. Discuss it with the children. Tell the children that the 12 apostles are sometimes called the 12 disciples. (Matthew 10:1–4) Next, show the children the New Testament time line (pages 76–77). Point out to the children where the stories of the books of Matthew and Mark appear on the time line. Sing "The Farmer and the Seed" on page 74. This song is about a parable Jesus told and goes along with the activity on page 10. Talk to the children about parables. Tell them that parables are stories that teach lessons. Jesus told many parables.

Flash Cards

Review flash cards 1–5. Then discuss flash cards 6–8.

Activity Pages

Give the children copies of activity pages 8–10 to complete either in class or at home. Be sure to explain the concepts to them and read any given story to or with the children so that they can successfully complete the activities.

Assignment

To further emphasize the parable of the farmer and the seed, let the children plant two or three pinto beans in a Styrofoam cup full of moist soil. Have the children take them home, care for them, and watch them grow.

Memory Verse

Jesus said, "Let the little children come to me . . . " (Matthew 19:14)

Baby Jesus

(Matthew 1:18–25; Luke 2)

An angel told Mary that she was going to have a baby boy. He would be God's Son. While Mary and Joseph were in Bethlehem, baby Jesus was born. There was no room in the inn, so Jesus was born in a stable. His bed was a manger. Write the words in the puzzle that match each picture.

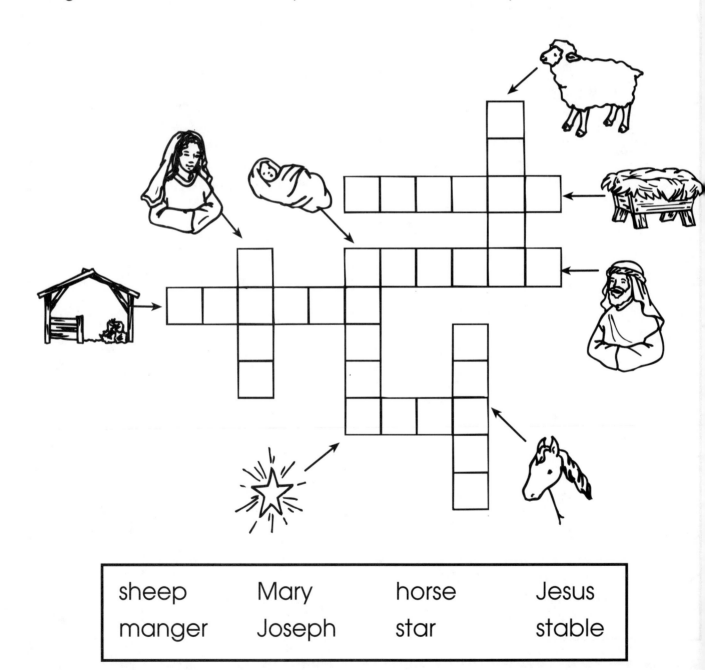

sheep	Mary	horse	Jesus
manger	Joseph	star	stable

Jesus Calms a Storm

(Mark 4:35-41)

Jesus had power over nature. He told the winds and the waves to be still, and they obeyed Him! Count by 2s to connect the dots. Color the picture.

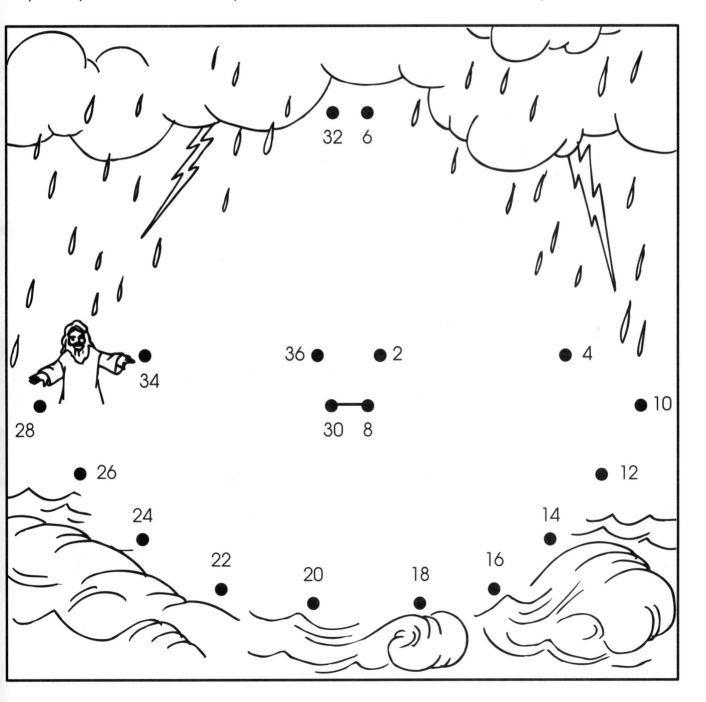

The Farmer and the Seed

(Mark 4:1-20)

Jesus was a wonderful storyteller. He told stories called *parables.* These kinds of stories help people learn important lessons. Find nine things that are wrong in the picture below. Circle them.

Unit 2 . . . . Luke & John

BUSINESS

(If there is any confusion about how to conduct class, refer to the Introduction and Unit 1 for greater detail.)

Welcome

Greet the children as they come in. Use the Bible Story Club password or handshake, if they have chosen one. Induct any new members.

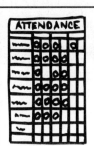 Attendance Charts

Give each child one sticker for attendance and one for bringing a Bible (or they can color in the squares).

Prayer Requests and Prayer

At this time, take prayer requests from the children. Honor these and then say a class prayer to begin the lesson.

LESSON

Lesson Introduction

Sing one of the songs on page 73. Children may look at the chart from the back of the book to help them remember the order of the New Testament books. Review flash cards 1–8 and "The 12 Apostles" chart before introducing today's lesson. Reviewing the flash cards from previous lessons every time will help the children memorize the facts.

Lesson

Show the children the books of Luke and John in the Bible. Tell them that these are the last two of the four gospels, and remind them that *gospel* means "good news." Remind the children that all four gospels tell the same story of the life of Jesus, each in its own way.

Lesson continued

Luke—This gospel was written by Luke, a doctor. Luke traveled with Paul on some of his missionary journeys, preaching the good news about Jesus. This book tells the story of Jesus from His birth to His death, resurrection, and ascension into heaven. Children are always fascinated by the stories of the miracles that Jesus did. (Show flash card 9 and discuss some of these.)

John—This gospel was written by the apostle John. John's brother was James, and they were fishermen. This gospel is somewhat different from the other three. He tells why Jesus came to earth. He wrote these things so that we might believe that Jesus is really the Son of God!

Point out to the children where these books appear on the time line. Sing "Jesus Is God's Son" on page 74.

Flash Cards

Discuss flash cards 10 and 11.

 Activity Pages

Give the children copies of activity pages 13–15 to complete either in class or at home. Explain the concepts to the children and read the stories to or with them. The children will need green construction paper for page 14. For page 15, cut two lengths of yarn for each child. You may want to reinforce the holes with tape. Make sure each child understands how to make the picture of Jesus go up and down.

Assignment

Jesus ascended into heaven. To help the children better understand the concept of Jesus ascending into heaven, give each child a balloon filled with helium. Draw Jesus' face on each one, or attach a drawing of Jesus to each one. Have the children take the balloons outside and let them float up into the clouds.

Memory Verse

And Jesus grew in wisdom and stature, and in favor with God and men. (Luke 2:52)

Jesus at the Temple

(Luke 2:41-52)

When Jesus was 12 years old, He went to Jerusalem with His parents. On the way home, they couldn't find Jesus. Help Mary and Joseph find Jesus.

People Praise Jesus

(John 12:12-15)

When Jesus came into Jerusalem riding on a donkey, the people spread their coats and palm branches down on the road. They praised Jesus saying, "Blessed is the King of Israel!" Cut out the palm leaf pattern below. Trace around it on green construction paper. Then cut it out and cut many short notches on the sides of the leaf. Wave it saying words of praise about Jesus. Or, write some words of praise on the center of the leaf.

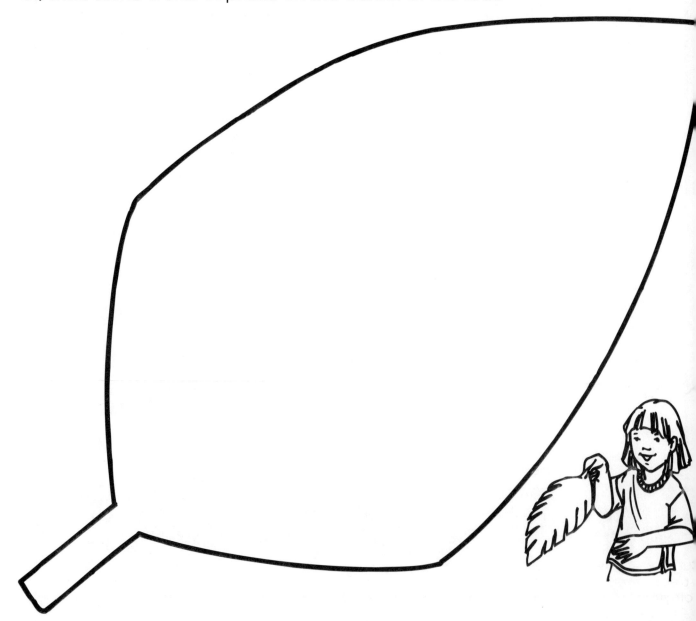

Name _____

Jesus Is Alive!

(Luke 24:50-53)

After Jesus died, God made Him come to life again! One day, while Jesus was talking to His disciples, He was taken up into heaven to live with God. The disciples were filled with joy!

Cut on the dotted lines. Punch holes in the black circles. Tie a piece of yarn to each end of the Jesus pattern. Thread both strings through the holes in the picture and tie in back. Pull the string to make Jesus go up in the clouds.

BUSINESS

(If there is any confusion about how to conduct class, refer to the Introduction and Unit 1 for greater detail.)

 ### Welcome

Greet the children as they come in. Use the Bible Story Club password or handshake, if they have chosen one. Induct any new members.

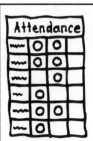 ### Attendance Charts

Give each child one sticker for attendance and one for bringing a Bible (or they can color in the squares).

Prayer Requests and Prayer

At this time, take prayer requests from the children. Honor these and then say a class prayer to begin the lesson.

LESSON

 ### Lesson Introduction

Sing one of the songs on page 73. Using the chart in the back of the book, point to each book of the New Testament as you sing. Review flash cards 1–11 before introducing today's lesson. This is very important! You will see by the end of the book that the children have memorized many facts because the flash cards will be so familiar to them.

 ### Lesson

Show the children the book of Acts in the Bible. Tell them that Luke, the doctor, wrote this book. Acts begins where the gospel of Luke ends. Remind the children that we can remember what each book of the Bible is about by its title.

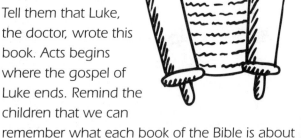

Lesson continued

Acts—This book tells about the acts of the apostles. In other words, it tells about the things the apostles did after Jesus went up to heaven.

Acts is a very important book. Give the children an overview of its contents which include these highlights:

- Jesus' ascension retold (Acts 1)

- Matthias chosen to replace Judas (Acts 1)

- Peter's sermon at Pentecost; the church begins. (Acts 2)

- Peter heals a lame man; Peter and John are put in jail. (Acts 3, 4)

- The apostles spread the good news of Jesus. (Acts 5–8)

- Many people become Christians. (Acts 2:41; 4:4; 8–10; 16)

- Christians are persecuted: put in prison, beaten, or killed. (Acts 5:18,40; 7:54–8:3)

- Paul (first called Saul) becomes a Christian; goes on three missionary journeys; establishes churches in many towns; is shipwrecked; goes to Rome. (Acts 9; 13–28)

Point out to the children where these stories appear on the time line. Sing "The Apostles" song on page 74, which goes along with activity page 18.

 ## Flash Cards

Discuss flash cards 12 and 13.

 ## Activity Pages

Give the children copies of activity pages 18–20 to complete either in class or at home. Explain the concepts to the children and read the stories to or with them. You will need to provide craft sticks and construction paper for page 18. Children may need help drawing around their hands. For page 19, each child will need a sheet of construction paper on which to glue the puzzle.

Be sure to read the featured stories with the children and discuss them. For page 20, the children will need to be familiar with the story of Paul.

 ## Assignment

Discuss the memory verse with the children. This week, ask the children if they would like to pretend to be an apostle. They might dress up in a bathrobe with a small towel over their heads. Then suggest that they tell their families the good news—that Jesus is our Savior!

Memory Verse

. . . they never stopped teaching and proclaiming the good news that Jesus is the Christ. (Acts 5:42)

The 13th Apostle

(Acts 1:13–26)

Jesus chose 12 special men to be His helpers. Later, Judas died, and there were only 11. Peter said they must choose another man to take Judas' place. They chose Matthias.

On construction paper, draw around both of your hands. Cut them out. Glue a wooden craft stick behind each hand as shown. Draw faces on each finger. Then draw a face on one end of each stick to make the 12 apostles. Fold one thumb down. Draw another face on the back of it. When that thumb is down, it's Judas. When it's up, it's Matthias!

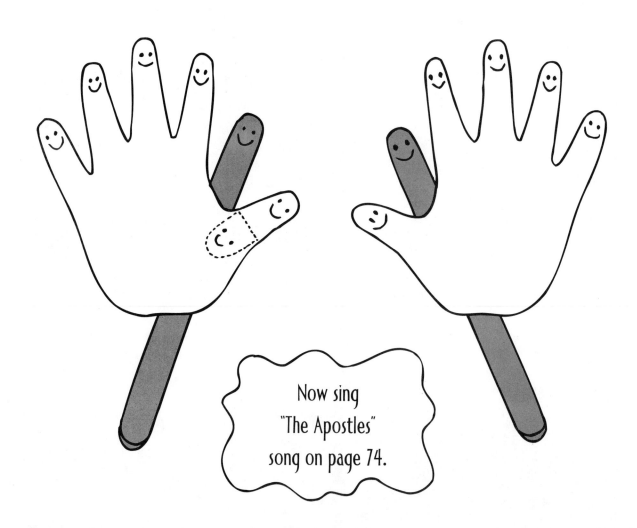

Now sing
"The Apostles"
song on page 74.

SS20001

A Puzzle Chain

Below are pictures that show some of the stories found in the book of Acts.
Color and carefully cut out each puzzle piece. Then fit them together,
matching the edges. Glue the puzzle chain on a piece of construction paper.

Apostles preach good news.

Paul's missionary journeys

Pentecost: The church begins.

People become Christians.

Christians are persecuted.

Peter heals a lame man.

SS200015

Paul Becomes a Christian

(Acts 9:1–22)

Jesus had a special job for Paul. He became a great missionary! Color and cut out the number pictures below. Mix them up, put them back in order, and tell someone the story.

Paul persecutes and jails Christians.

Paul is blinded by a bright light.

Paul is led to Damascus.

Ananias lays his hands on Paul to restore his sight.

Paul is baptized.

Paul preaches.

SS20001

Unit 4 .... Romans and 1 & 2 Corinthians

BUSINESS

(If there is any confusion about how to conduct class, refer to the Introduction and Unit 1 for greater detail.)

 ### Welcome

Greet the children as they come in. Use the Bible Story Club password or handshake, if they have chosen one. Induct any new members.

 ### Attendance Charts

Give each child one sticker for attendance and one for bringing a Bible (or they can color in the squares).

 ### Prayer Requests and Prayer

At this time, take prayer requests from the children. Honor these and then say a class prayer to begin the lesson.

LESSON

 ### Lesson Introduction

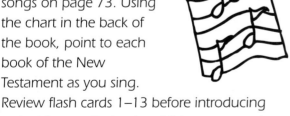

Sing one of the songs on page 73. Using the chart in the back of the book, point to each book of the New Testament as you sing. Review flash cards 1–13 before introducing today's lesson. Praise the children over and over for their efforts in memorizing the flash cards. Tell them that you are proud of them!

Lesson

Show the children the books of Romans and 1 & 2 Corinthians in the Bible.

These books are letters that Paul wrote. Paul's letters are sometimes called epistles. Remind them that the titles of the books give us clues about what is in the books.

 ## Lesson continued

Romans—This book is Paul's letter to the church in Rome. Paul had not yet been to Rome, but he planned to go there someday. The main reason for Paul's letter was to explain that everybody sins, but Jesus saves us from our sins. Sin is doing what is wrong. Sin means breaking God's laws. We must be thankful that Jesus died for us and that God is willing to forgive us. (Romans 3:22–24)

1 & 2 Corinthians—These books are Paul's letters to the church in the city of Corinth. Paul helped the Corinthians solve church problems. He explained to them how to correctly observe the Lord's Supper. (1 Corinthians 11:17–34) Paul also encouraged them to give generously of their money to help people in need. (1 Corinthians 16; 2 Corinthians 8,9) 1 Corinthians 13 is the chapter of love. Read verses 4–7 to the children. Point out to them that love is not just a feeling, it is an action. Love changes the way we behave!

Point out to the children where these books appear on the time line. Sing "Be a Cheerful Giver" on page 74.

 ## Flash Cards

Discuss flash cards 14–16.

 ## Activity Pages

Give the children copies of activity pages 23–25 to complete either in class or at home. Explain the concepts to the children and read the stories to or with them. Use page 24 as a discussion page. You can cut out the strips and let small groups of children discuss these situations. Or, make a copy for each child to color and take home to share with his or her family. On page 25, help the children glue only the sides of the basket together so that the money can be put inside.

Assignment

Paul reminded the Corinthians that God loves a cheerful giver. Bring a piggy bank or decorated coffee can to class. Tell the children that they are invited to bring their pennies to give to the Lord. Let the children put their pennies in the bank each week. At the end of this series of lessons, present the offering to someone in need.

 ## Memory Verse

Love is patient, love is kind . . .
(1 Corinthians 13:4)

You've Got Mail

(Romans 1:1, 7–10)

Many of the books of the New Testament are really letters that Paul or others wrote. Sometimes the letters were written for one person, and sometimes they were written for whole churches. Pretend you are Paul. Write a letter or draw a picture to tell your church something you think God wants them to know or do.

What Is Sin?

(Romans 3:22-24; 6:23)

The book of Romans tells us that everybody sins, but Jesus saves us from our sins. God forgives us because Jesus died for us. Sin is doing what is wrong. Loo at the cartoons below and answer the questions.

What is the sin?

What should he have done?

What is the sin?

What should she have done?

What is the sin?

What should he have done?

SS2000

Giving

(1 Corinthians 16:2,3; 2 Corinthians 9:7,8)

Corinthians 9:7 says *. . . God loves a cheerful giver.* God gives us money to
uy the things we need. He also expects us to give some of our money back
Him. This money helps the church and helps needy people. Color the
asket and cut it out. Fold the basket. Glue only the sides together. Cut out
e money and put it in the collection basket. What does it mean to be a
heerful giver?

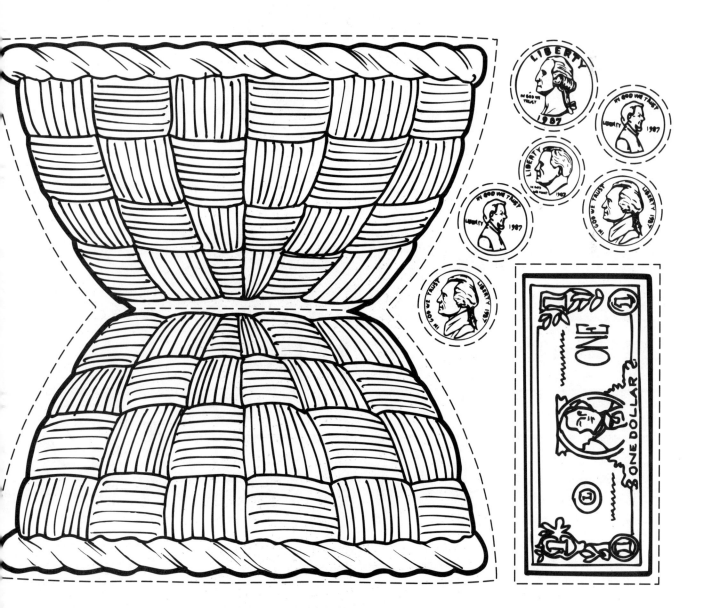

Unit 5 . . . Galatians & Ephesians

BUSINESS

(If there is any confusion about how to conduct class, refer to the Introduction and Unit 1 for greater detail.)

 ### Welcome

Greet the children as they come in. Use the Bible Story Club password or handshake, if they have chosen one. Induct any new members.

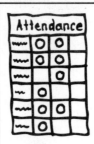 ### Attendance Charts

Give each child one sticker for attendance and one for bringing a Bible (or they can color in the squares).

 ### Prayer Requests and Prayer

At this time, take prayer requests from the children. Honor these and then say a class prayer to begin the lesson.

LESSON

 ### Lesson Introduction

Sing one of the songs on page 73. Using the chart in the back of the book, point to each book of the New Testament as you sing. Review flash cards 1–16 before introducing today's lesson. Give each child a small reward, such as gum, candy, or stickers, for the progress the children are making with the flash cards.

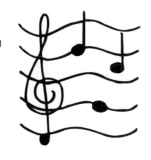

 ### Lesson

Show the children the books of Galatians and Ephesians in the Bible. Tell them that these books are letters (epistles) that Paul wrote. Later on, they became books in the New Testament. Tell the children that we can remember what each book of the Bible is about by its title.

Lesson continued

Galatians—This book is Paul's letter to the churches in the region of Galatia. In this letter, Paul explains that in the past, the Jews were God's chosen people, and they were commanded to obey the old law. Now God's chosen people are Christians and are no longer commanded to obey the old law. Instead, Christians must obey the laws of Jesus Christ. Some people did not understand this change of laws. They still tried to obey the old law, even though they were Christians now. The book of Galatians also includes a list of the fruits of the Spirit. Read these to the children in Galatians 5:22,23, and discuss what they mean.

Ephesians—This book is Paul's letter to the church in Ephesus. The message of Ephesians is that Christians are saved by the goodness and kindness of God. That is what we call grace. God forgives our sins even though we don't deserve it. That is God's gift to us! Ephesians also tells us that Jesus is the head of the church. The church belongs to Jesus because He died on the cross. In a way, He bought the church with His own blood! Ephesians 6:10–17 is a word picture. It describes the armor of God, which is the power God gives Christians to overcome the ways of the devil. Read that passage of Scripture to the children and discuss it.

Point out to the children where these books appear on the time line. Sing "The Ephesians Song" on page 74. (It goes along with activity page 30.)

Flash Cards

 Discuss flash cards 17 and 18.

Activity Pages

 Give the children copies of activity pages 28–30 to complete either in class or at home. Explain the concepts to the children and read the stories to or with them. For the activity on page 30, you may want to use the songs on page 74 that the children learned in previous lessons. They may also want to sing other Bible songs that they know.

Assignment

 One of the fruits of the Spirit is kindness. Sometimes we see on the news that someone has done something bad. Reporters call it a random act of violence. This week, tell the children to do a random act of kindness for someone and tell about it next week.

Memory Verse

 . . . *Sing and make music in your heart to the Lord.* (Ephesians 5:19)

Fruits of the Spirit

(Galatians 5:22,23)

God tells us in Galatians that we must have the fruits of the Spirit. They are love, joy, peace, patience, kindness, goodness, faithfulness, gentleness, and self-control. Draw nine fruits below. Write a fruit of the Spirit on each fruit.

SS200

The Armor of God

(Ephesians 6:13-17)

phesians 6 tells us that the devil is always trying to make us sin. God tells us ow we can protect ourselves from the devil. Just like a soldier, we should arm urselves with the helmet of salvation, the shield of faith, the belt of truth, the reastplate of righteousness, the sword of the Spirit, and have our feet fitted ith the gospel of peace. Color the pictures below. Cut out the armor. Glue it n the soldier.

Sing to the Lord

(Ephesians 5:19)

Ephesians 5:19 tells us to sing and make music in our hearts to the Lord. Color and cut out one of the bracelets. Wrap it around your wrist and tape it together. Now make a fist like the one shown in the picture. Draw two eyes on your hand with a washable marker. Wiggle your thumb back and forth to make your hand puppet sing Bible songs that you know!

Can your puppet sing "The Books of the New Testament" song?

SS2000

Unit 6 . . . . Philippians & Colossians

BUSINESS

(If there is any confusion about how to conduct class, refer to the Introduction and Unit 1 for greater detail.)

 ### Welcome

Greet the children as they come in. Use the Bible Story Club password or handshake, if they have chosen one. Induct any new members.

 ### Attendance Charts

Give each child one sticker for attendance and one for bringing a Bible (or they can color in the squares).

 ### Prayer Requests and Prayer

At this time, take prayer requests from the children. Honor these and then say a class prayer to begin the lesson.

LESSON

 ### Lesson Introduction

Sing one of the songs on page 73. Using the chart in the back of the book, point to each book of the New Testament as you sing. Review flash cards 1–18 before introducing today's lesson. The children should be able to recall the first few flash cards very easily now that they have practiced them so many times.

 ### Lesson

Show the children the books of Philippians and Colossians in the Bible. Tell them that these books are letters (epistles) that Paul wrote. Later on, they became books in the New Testament. Tell the children that we can remember what each book of the Bible is about by its title.

 ## Lesson continued

Philippians—This book is Paul's letter to the church in Philippi. It is a thank-you letter to them for the gifts and support they sent to Paul. Philippians is known as the letter of joy. Read Philippians 4:4 to the children. The word *joy* or *rejoice* occurs about 16 times in the book. Help the children remember this with the following memory device: Picture someone flipping for joy . . . FLIPpians!

Colossians—This book is Paul's letter to the church in Colosse. One of Paul's friends, Epaphras, helped start this church. Epaphras told Paul about the Christians there, and Paul wrote them this letter. Paul told them that Jesus has all power and authority. He is truly God's Son, and God made Jesus to be the head of the church. Jesus is the greatest person who ever lived! (chapter 1) Colossians contains good rules for Christians to live by. (chapter 3) Paul explains how fathers, mothers, and children can live together as a happy family.

Point out to the children where these books appear on the time line. Sing "This Is the Way We Talk to God" on page 74. (This song goes along with activity page 34.)

 ## Flash Cards

Discuss flash cards 19 and 20.

 ## Activity Pages

Give the children copies of activity pages 33–35 to complete either in class or at home. Explain the concepts to the children and read the stories to or with them.

 ## Assignment

Colossians 3 tells us how to have happy families. This week, suggest that the children ask their parents to have a family night. They might go to a movie, have a cookout, play a game, or do something else that the whole family likes to do. Remind the children to do what their memory verse says when they have their family night.

Memory Verse

Children, obey your parents in everything, for this pleases the Lord.
(Colossians 3:20)

The Letter of Joy
(Philippians 4:4)

The book of Philippians is sometimes called the letter of joy. In the Bible verse below, add to find each number. Then write the word that has the same number in the blank.

16 = in
12 = always
17 = again
13 = Rejoice
15 = say
11 = I
10 = Lord
18 = it
14 = the
20 = will

_____ _____ _____ _____ _____.
8 + 5   7 + 9   6 + 8   5 + 5   6 + 6

___ ___ _____ _____ _____ : _____!
4 + 7 10 + 10   8 + 7   9 + 9   8 + 9   6 + 7

(Philippians 4:4)

What makes you have joy? Write three things below that make you feel joyful!

1. _____   2. _____   3. _____

Talking to God

(Philippians 4:6; Colossians 4:2)

God tells us in the book of Philippians to pray with thanksgiving. He wants us to talk to Him. He is our Father, and He gives us what we need. We should always remember to be thankful. The Bible verse below is from Colossians. Use the letters in the verse to spell words that tell what you thank God for. How many words can you make? Two examples are given for you. Remember, don't use any letters that are not in the Bible verse.

Devote yourselves to prayer, being . . . thankful.

(Colossians 4:2)

_____toys_____   _____   _____

_____parents_____   _____   _____

_____   _____   _____

_____   _____   _____

_____   _____   _____

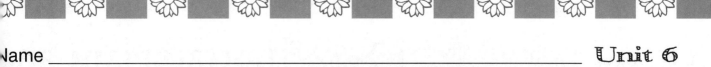

Happy Families

(Colossians 3:18-20)

Colossians 3:18–20 tells us rules to follow that will help us have happy families. What are the rules for fathers, mothers, and children? Write five rules your family has. Draw a picture of your family following one of the rules.

1. _____

2. _____

3. _____

4. _____

5. _____

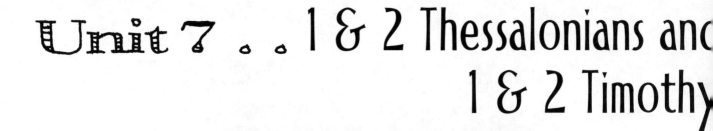

Unit 7 . . 1 & 2 Thessalonians and 1 & 2 Timothy

BUSINESS

(If there is any confusion about how to conduct class, refer to the Introduction and Unit 1 for greater detail.)

 ### Welcome

Greet the children as they come in. Use the Bible Story Club password or handshake, if they have chosen one. Induct any new members.

 ### Attendance Charts

Give each child one sticker for attendance and one for bringing a Bible (or they can color in the squares).

Prayer Requests and Prayer

At this time, take prayer requests from the children. Honor these and then say a class prayer to begin the lesson.

LESSON

 ### Lesson Introduction

Sing one of the songs on page 73. Using the chart in the back of the book, point to each book of the New Testament as you sing. Review flash cards 1–20 before introducing today's lesson. You may want to spend more time reviewing flash cards from the most recent lessons if you see that the children can recite the earlier ones with ease.

Lesson

Show the children the books of 1 & 2 Thessalonians and 1 & 2 Timothy in the Bible. Remind the children that these books are letters (epistles) written by Paul. Later on, they became books in the New Testament. Tell the children that we can remember what each book of the Bible is about by its title.

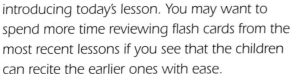

Lesson continued

1 & 2 Thessalonians—These books are Paul's letters to the church in Thessalonica. Paul wrote to praise these Christians for their faith in Jesus and to encourage them to continue to live their lives in a way that would please God. The most encouraging thing Paul wrote was that Jesus would come again someday. Read 1 Thessalonians 4:13–18 to find out what the second coming will be like!

1 & 2 Timothy—These books are Paul's letters to his young friend, Timothy. Timothy was taught the Word of God by his mother, Eunice, and his grandmother, Lois. (2 Timothy 1:5) When Timothy grew up, he became a preacher. (2 Timothy 4:2–5) He went on some of Paul's missionary journeys. At one time, he was the preacher for the Ephesian church. (1 Timothy 1:3) Paul told Timothy to continue to grow in faith and to preach the good news of Jesus. He explained to Timothy how to appoint church leaders.

Point out to the children where these books appear on the time line. Sing "When I Grow Up" on page 75.

Flash Cards

Discuss flash cards 21 and 22.

Activity Pages

Give the children copies of activity pages 38–40 to complete either in class or at home. Explain the concepts to the children and read the stories listed to or with them. Tell the children to be sure that they glue page 38 directly over page 39 so that the pictures behind the windows line up correctly.

Assignment

Paul and Timothy were missionaries, preaching the good news in many countries. Find out if your church supports missionaries in other places in the world. Find the locations on a map. This week, have the children make cards to encourage these missionaries. Send a sheet of stationery or manila paper home with each child to make a card. Tell them to bring their cards next week so that you can mail them all in one large envelope.

Memory Verse

. . . never tire of doing what is right.
(2 Thessalonians 3:13)

Name _____ Unit 7

Jesus Is Coming Again

(1 Thessalonians 4:14–17)

1 & 2 Thessalonians tell us that someday, Jesus will come to earth again to take Christians to heaven to live with Him forever! Color the pictures on this page and page 39. Cut only on the dotted lines so that the doors and windows can open. Glue this page on top of page 39 to see who is watching for Jesus' return.

Jesus Is Coming Again

continued

Name _____

When I Grow Up

(1 Timothy 4:12,13; 2 Timothy 1:5; 3:14,15)

Timothy's mother and grandmother taught him the Bible when he was very young. Timothy grew up to be a preacher. What do you want to be when you grow up? Draw your answer in the picture frame below.

         SS2000

Unit 8 . . . . . . Titus & Philemon

BUSINESS

(If there is any confusion about how to conduct class, refer to the Introduction and Unit 1 for greater detail.)

 ### Welcome

Greet the children as they come in. Use the Bible Story Club password or handshake, if they have chosen one. Induct any new members.

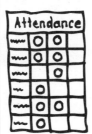 ### Attendance Charts

Give each child one sticker for attendance and one for bringing a Bible (or they can color in the squares).

 ### Prayer Requests and Prayer

At this time, take prayer requests from the children. Honor these and then say a class prayer to begin the lesson.

LESSON

 ### Lesson Introduction

Sing one of the songs on page 73. Using the chart in the back of the book, point to each book of the New Testament as you sing. Review flash cards 1–22 before introducing today's lesson. You may want to spend more time reviewing flash cards from the most recent lessons if you see that the children can recite the earlier ones with ease.

 ### Lesson

Show the children the books of Titus and Philemon in the Bible. Tell them that these books are letters (epistles) written by Paul. Later on, they became books in the New Testament. Tell the children that we can remember what each book of the Bible is about by its title.

Lesson continued

Titus—This book is Paul's letter to another preacher named Titus. Sometimes Titus traveled with Paul on his missionary journeys. Paul left him on the island of Crete to help the church there get organized. Titus appointed elders there and preached. (Titus 1:5) Paul told Titus to continue to teach the truth of God's Word. He also encouraged the Christians there to do good to others. (Titus 2:7,14; 3:1,8,14) Discuss with the children some examples of doing good for others.

Philemon—This book is Paul's letter to a man named Philemon. Philemon owned a slave whose name was Onesimus. Onesimus ran away. Later, he became a Christian and was sorry for the wrong he had done. Paul wrote to Philemon and explained that Onesimus was sorry about what he had done and was coming back to him. Paul asked Philemon to forgive Onesimus and welcome him back, not only as his slave, but now as a Christian brother. The Bible tells us that just as God forgives us, so we should forgive others.

Point out to the children where these books appear on the time line. Sing "Doing Good" on page 75. (This song goes along with activity pages 43 and 44.)

Flash Cards

Discuss flash cards 23 and 24.

Activity Pages

Give the children copies of activity pages 43–45 to complete either in class or at home. Explain the concepts to the children and read the stories to or with them. The paper dolls on page 45 might be sturdier if glued to tagboard before they are cut out.

Assignment

Being a helper is doing what is good. Make a helping "coupon" for each child before class. The coupons should say, "I will be your helper." (See sample coupon below.) Give each child one to give to someone this week. Tell the children to give it to their moms, dads, grandparents, neighbors, or teachers. They should tell the person that whenever they need a helper, they can cash their coupon in, and the child will be willing to help.

Memory Verse

. . . be ready to do whatever is good.
(Titus 3:1)

I WILL BE YOUR HELPER

SS2000

Name _____ Unit 8

Doing Good

(Titus 3:1, 8, 14)

Titus 3:1 says to be ready to do whatever is good. What are some good things you can do? To find out, fill in the missing letters in each line below with the beginning letter of each picture.

On the back, write one more way you can do good.

___hare your toy___.

___ive to the needy.

V___s___t the s___ck.

Obey you___ pa___ents.

He___p an e___der___y person.

Forgive a___ e___emy.

B___ a fri___nd to som___on___.

Name _____ Unit 8

I Can Help

(Titus 3:8)

Another way to do what is good is to be a good helper. Look at the children who are helping in the picture below. Some parts of the picture are not finished. Finish the drawings. Then color the pictures. What can you do to help?

Onesimus Runs Away

(Philemon verses 10-19)

Onesimus was a slave. He ran away from his master, Philemon. Later, Onesimus became a Christian. He was sorry that he had run away. He went back to his master, Philemon. Paul wrote a letter to Philemon asking him to forgive Onesimus. Just as God forgives us, so must we forgive others.

Color and cut out the paper dolls. Fold back the tabs to make Paul and Philemon stand up. Put your fingers through the holes to make Onesimus run away from Philemon and back again.

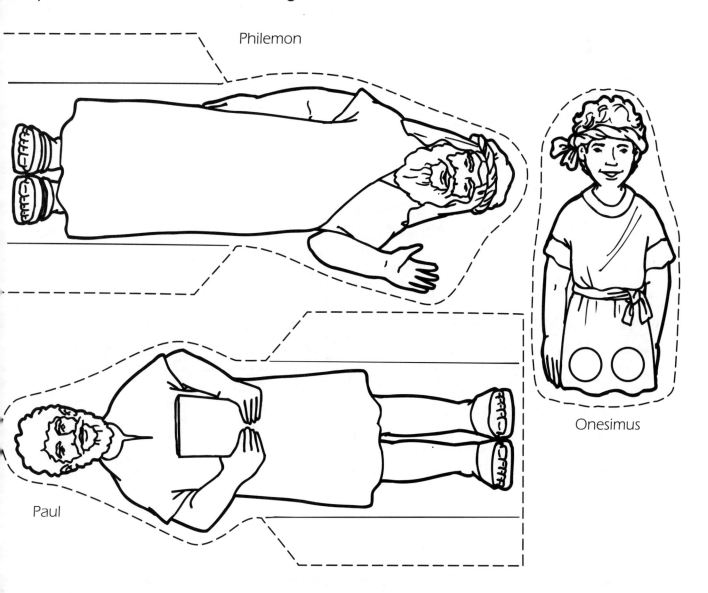

Philemon

Onesimus

Paul

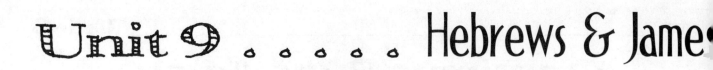

Unit 9 . . . . . Hebrews & James

BUSINESS

(If there is any confusion about how to conduct class, refer to the Introduction and Unit 1 for greater detail.)

Welcome

Greet the children as they come in. Use the Bible Story Club password or handshake, if they have chosen one. Induct any new members.

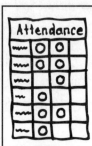

Attendance Charts

Give each child one sticker for attendance and one for bringing a Bible (or they can color in the squares).

Prayer Requests and Prayer

At this time, take prayer requests from the children. Honor these and then say a class prayer to begin the lesson.

LESSON

Lesson Introduction

Sing one of the songs on page 73. Using the chart in the back of the book, point to each book of the New Testament as you sing. Review flash cards 1–24 before introducing today's lesson. If time allows, divide the class into two teams, and let them have a contest over the facts on the flash cards. Remember to praise the children for learning so much information about God's Word.

Lesson

Show the children the books of Hebrews and James in the Bible. These books are also letters (epistles). Remind the children that we can remember what each book of the Bible is about by its title.

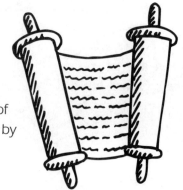

SS2000

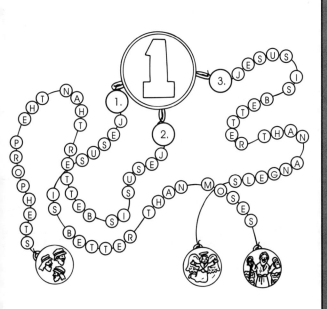

Lesson continued

Hebrews—It is not known who wrote this letter. Hebrews is another name for Jews. This book was written to explain to the Jews that a new law had come and that they were no longer under the old law of Moses. Hebrews is called "the book of better things." Jesus is better than Moses and the prophets of the Old Testament. Jesus is better than angels. The new law of Jesus is better than the old law of Moses. Jesus is the best!

James—This letter is written by James, the brother of Jesus, not James the apostle. (Matthew 13:55) James is a little book full of good advice for living the Christian life. The main idea in James is that if you believe in Jesus (faith), you must show it by the good things you do (works). Read James 2:14–24 to the children to help them understand this idea. James also points out that all the good things we enjoy are gifts from God, our Father.

Point out to the children where these books appear on the time line. Sing "The Faith Song" on page 75.

Flash Cards

Discuss flash cards 25 and 26.

Activity Pages

Give the children copies of activity pages 48–50 to complete either in class or at home. Explain the concepts to the children and read the stories to or with them. For pages 49 and 50, you will need magazines from which the children may cut pictures.

Assignment

One of the good gifts God gives us is food to eat. Bring a snack to class and let each child say a short prayer of thanks to God. This week, remind the children to say a prayer before each meal thanking God for His wonderful gifts.

Memory Verse

Every good and perfect gift is from above, coming down from the Father . . . (James 1:17)

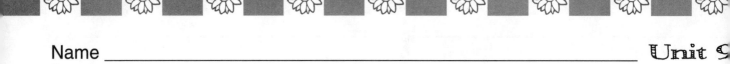

Name _____ Unit 9

Hebrews

(Hebrews 1:1,4; 3:3; 6:9)

The book of Hebrews is often called "the book of better things." Jesus is #1. He is the Son of God. To find out what the book of Hebrews says about Jesus, follow the three sets of beads. Write the letters from each set in order on the blanks below.

1. __ __ __ __ __ __   __ __   __ __ __ __ __   __ __ __ __

     __ __ __ __ __.

2. __ __ __ __ __ __   __ __   __ __ __ __ __ __ __   __ __ __

     __ __ __   __ __ __ __ __ __ __ __.

3. __ __ __ __ __ __   __ __   __ __ __ __ __ __ __   __ __ __ __

     __ __ __ __ __ __ __.

What Is Faith?

(James 2:14-17)

you love Jesus and believe in Him, you must show it by doing good things for
ther people. This is the message in James. Think of some things you could
ive to help needy people. Cut out or draw pictures of these things and glue
hem in the box below. Think how happy someone would be to get these
hings!

Name _____

Gifts From God

(James 1:17; Romans 8:32)

James 1:17 says, *Every good and perfect gift is from above, coming down from the Father . . .* The best gift God has given us is Jesus! What other good gifts has God given you? Draw or cut out pictures from magazines of gifts God has given you. Glue them in the box. Color the bow and ribbon. Finish the prayer.

Thank You, God, for _____

_____

_____

_____ .

       SS2000

Unit 10 . . . . 1 & 2 Peter

BUSINESS

(If there is any confusion about how to conduct class, refer to the Introduction and Unit 1 for greater detail.)

Welcome

Greet the children as they come in. Use the Bible Story Club password or handshake, if they have chosen one. Induct any new members.

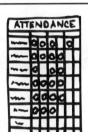

Attendance Charts

Give each child one sticker for attendance and one for bringing a Bible (or they can color in the squares).

Prayer Requests and Prayer

At this time, take prayer requests from the children. Honor these and then say a class prayer to begin the lesson.

LESSON

Lesson Introduction

Sing one of the songs on page 73. Using the chart in the back of the book, point to each book of the New Testament as you sing. Review flash cards 1–26 before introducing today's lesson. Spend more time reviewing flash cards from the most recent lessons if you see that the children can recite the earlier ones with ease.

Lesson

Show the children the books of 1 & 2 Peter in the Bible. Tell the children that these books are letters (epistles) written by Peter, the apostle. Remind the children that Peter was a close friend of Jesus. After Jesus died, Peter was the one who preached to the crowds on the day of Pentecost, the day the church began. Peter continued preaching the good news that Jesus Christ died to save people from their sins. Tell the children that the title of these books will help them remember that Peter wrote them.

Lesson continued

1 & 2 Peter—Peter wrote these letters to Christians teaching them that they are a holy nation, specially chosen by God to be His people. One of the lessons Peter teaches is that Christians must obey those in authority. That means we should obey the laws made by the government and the police officers who enforce the laws. We must obey our parents, grandparents, and teachers. Obedience shows that you have respect for the people who take care of you.

Another lesson Peter teaches is that sometimes we will suffer for doing what is right. Other people may sometimes make fun of us for going to church or for living the Christian life. We must love God and do what is right anyway. Look what Jesus did. He always did what was right even when people did bad things to Him. When that happens to us, we should think, "What would Jesus do?"

Help the children find where these books appear on the time line. Sing "I Will Follow Jesus" on page 75.

Flash Card

Discuss flash card 27.

Activity Pages

Give the children copies of activity pages 53–55 to complete either in class or at home. Explain the concepts to the children and read the stories to or with them. Optional: You may purchase WWJD bracelets or pencils for each child to go along with this lesson.

Assignment

This week, ask the children to imitate Jesus in everything they do. Talk about what they will be doing this week (going to school, playing with friends, helping at home, etc.). Remind them to stop and think each day about how to act. Encourage them to ask themselves, "What would Jesus do?," in their daily living. Tell them to be prepared to share their experiences with the class next week.

Memory Verse

Show proper respect to everyone . . .
(1 Peter 2:17)

Who Was Peter?

(Matthew 4:18; 10:2; 14:28, 29; Acts 2:1,14)

Peter wrote the books of 1 & 2 Peter.
He was one of Jesus' closest friends.
Write the letter of the correct answer in
the box at the end of each sentence.
The Bible verses will help you.

1. Peter was one of the twelve

   (r) tribes.   (s) apostles.   (t) rabbits.

2. Peter was a

   (g) doctor.   (h) pilot.   (i) fisherman.

3. Peter's brother's name was

   (l) Judas.   (m) Andrew.   (n) Fred.

4. One time, Jesus and Peter walked

   (o) on water.   (p) to Egypt.   (q) on the moon.

5. Peter and the other apostles preached to a large crowd on

   (m) Valentine's Day.   (n) Pentecost.   (o) Monday.

What was Peter's other
name? Write the letters
from the boxes to find out.

____ ____ ____ ____ ____

I Will Obey

(1 Peter 2:13-17)

In the book of 1 Peter, we read that God wants us to obey everyone who has
authority over us. We must be respectful. This pleases God. To find out some o
the people you should obey, use the letters in the shapes to finish the words.

1. I will obey my F ☐ △ H ◯ ✡ .

2. I will obey my M ⬠ △ H ◯ ✡ .

3. I will obey my △ ◯ ☐ CH ◯ ✡ .

4. I will obey my ◇ ☐ ◇ Y ⬡ I △ △ ◯ ✡ .

5. I will obey my G ✡ ☐ ✩ DP ☐ ✡ ◯ ✩ △ ⬡ .

6. I will obey P ⬠ LIC ◯ ⬠ FFIC ◯ ✡ ⬡ .

7. I will obey G ⬠ D.

Can you think of anyone else you need to obey? If so, write it below using the
shapes.

Follow in His Steps

(1 Peter 2:20,21)

n 1 Peter, we learn that we must sometimes suffer for doing what is right. We
hould follow in Jesus' steps and act just like Jesus would as much as we can.
Color, cut, and fold to make the booklet below.

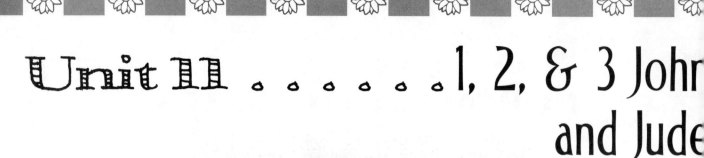

Unit 11 . . . . 1, 2, & 3 John and Jude

BUSINESS

(If there is any confusion about how to conduct class, refer to the Introduction and Unit 1 for greater detail.)

 ### Welcome

Greet the children as they come in. Use the Bible Story Club password or handshake, if they have chosen one. Induct any new members.

 ### Attendance Charts

Give each child one sticker for attendance and one for bringing a Bible (or they can color in the squares).

 ### Prayer Requests and Prayer

At this time, take prayer requests from the children. Honor these and then say a class prayer to begin the lesson.

LESSON

 ### Lesson Introduction

Sing one of the songs on page 73. Using the chart in the back of the book, point to each book of the New Testament as you sing. Review flash cards 1–27 before introducing today's lesson. Give more emphasis to the most recent ones. Remember to praise the children for their hard work.

 ### Lesson

Show the children the books of 1, 2, & 3 John and Jude in the Bible. Tell the children that these books are also letters (epistles). Remind the children that the titles of these books will help them remember who wrote them.

Lesson continued

1, 2, & 3 John—These letters were written by John, the apostle. Remind the children that John was a fisherman, the brother of James. He was also the author of the gospel of John. These books tell us all about love. God loves us, and we love Him. God wants us to love each other. John said, *For anyone who does not love his brother, whom he has seen, cannot love God, whom he has not seen.* (1 John 4:20) If we do love God, we must show it by obeying His commands. The word *love,* in its various forms, occurs over 50 times in these books!

For anyone who does not love his brother, whom he has seen, cannot love God, whom he has not seen.

(1 John 4:20)

Jude—The writer of this letter is probably Jude, the brother of Jesus and James. (Jude 1:1; Matthew 13:55) Jude wrote to tell Christians to watch out for false teachers. False teachers are people who try to change the Word of God. They try to convince people to believe in things that are not true. God says this is wrong. Jude encourages Christians to believe only God's truth.

Point out to the children where these books appear on the time line. Sing "God Loves Me and God Loves You" on page 75.

 ## Flash Cards

Discuss flash cards 28 and 29.

Activity Pages

Give the children copies of activity pages 58–60 to complete either in class or at home. Explain the concepts to the children and read the stories to or with them. On page 59, let the children color the stained-glass window with watercolor paints, markers, or crayons. You may want the children to tape them to your classroom window to let the light shine through them.

Assignment

No matter what time of year this lesson is taught, celebrate an "extra" Valentine's Day. Have the children cut out enough paper hearts so that each child has several. Have them write their names on each heart. Tell them to give the hearts to friends and family, saying "I love you" when they hand them their special valentine! Remind them that God wants us to love each other.

 ## Memory Verse

This is love for God: to obey his commands . . . (1 John 5:3)

What Is Love?

(1 John 4:7,9; 5:3)

Use the pictures in the box to learn what the book of 1 John says about love.

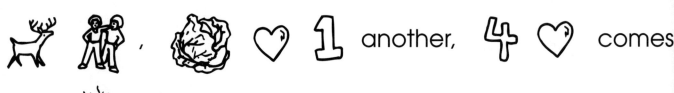

, another, comes

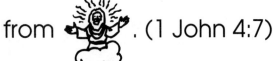

from . (1 John 4:7)

This is how showed his among us: He sent his

and only in the ... (1 John 4:9)

This is : obey his commands ... (1 John 5:3

SS200

Stained-Glass Window

(1 John 4:16)

Create a beautiful stained-glass window that has a very beautiful message from the book of 1 John!

1 = red
2 = blue
3 = green
4 = yellow
5 = purple

Jude's Message

(Jude verses 1, 4, 15, 20, 21, 25)

The book of Jude tells us, "Don't believe false teachers." False teachers change God's Word, and that is wrong!

Read the sentences below. If they are true, write TRUE in the blanks. If they are false, write FALSE in the blanks. (Hint: The Scriptures listed above can help you

1. God loves you.

_____

2. Jesus is not God's Son.

_____

3. God likes sin.

_____

4. We should pray.

_____

5. Eternal life in heaven is real.

_____

6. There is more than one God.

_____

7. It is okay to sin.

_____

8. God does not love you.

_____

9. Jesus is our Lord.

_____

Play this game: Take turns standing up and saying a sentence. Let the class te
if what you said is true or false. See if you can stump them!

SS2000

Unit 12 . . . . Revelation

BUSINESS

(If there is any confusion about how to conduct class, refer to the Introduction and Unit 1 for greater detail.)

Welcome

Greet the children as they come in. Use the Bible Story Club password or handshake, if they have chosen one. Induct any new members.

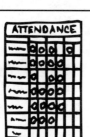

Attendance Charts
Give each child one sticker for attendance and one for bringing a Bible (or they can color in the squares).

Prayer Requests and Prayer

At this time, take prayer requests from the children. Honor these and then say a class prayer to begin the lesson.

LESSON

Lesson Introduction

Sing one of the songs on page 73. Using the chart in the back of the book, point to each book of the New Testament as you sing. Review flash cards 1–29 before introducing today's lesson. Give more emphasis to the most recent ones. Tell the children that they are studying the very last book of the Bible today. Praise them for all the hard work they have done.

Lesson
Show the children the book of Revelation in the Bible. This book was written by John, the apostle, who also wrote the gospel of John and 1, 2, & 3 John. The title of the book is a word that means "to reveal or uncover something," like a mystery or a secret.

Lesson continued

Revelation—John was sent to an island as a prisoner. He was being punished for being a Christian. Many Christians were being beaten, killed, or put in prison during this time in history. John saw a vision while he was on this island. A vision is like having a dream. God revealed the future in this vision. He showed John what would happen in the days to come. Because of the persecution, John wrote this book in a kind of secret code so that Christians could read it in safety. The main message of the book of Revelation is that although Satan will win some of the battles here on earth (sin and evil), God will win in the end. Good wins over evil. God is stronger than Satan. John also saw a vision of heaven. He tells us how wonderful heaven is and that God, Jesus, and the angels live there. If we obey God's commands, we will live in heaven someday, too!

Help the children find this book on the time line. Sing "Revelation" on page 75.

Flash Card

Discuss flash card 30.

Activity Pages

Give the children copies of activity pages 63–65 to complete either in class or at home. Explain the concepts to the children and read the stories to or with them. You will need to read the featured verses on pages 63 and 65 before the children can complete these activities.

Assignment

This week, have the children deliver invitations to their parents if you plan to have a program or party at the completion of this book. The purpose of the program is to show parents what their children have learned using the flash cards, charts, and time line. Next week, you can review all the lessons and practice for the program.

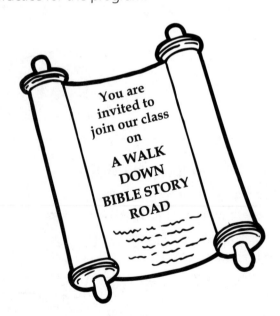

You are invited to join our class on
A WALK DOWN BIBLE STORY ROAD

Memory Verse

. . ."*Great and marvelous are your deeds, Lord God Almighty . . .*" (Revelation 15:3)

SS200

Who Was John?

(Matthew 10:2-4; Mark 1:19, 20; Revelation 1:1; John 19:26, 27)

The Bible tells us a lot of information about John. John was a great man. Read the questions about John on the heart. Then cut out the puzzle pieces. Glue them onto the heart, matching the shapes. Then you will know the answers to the questions.

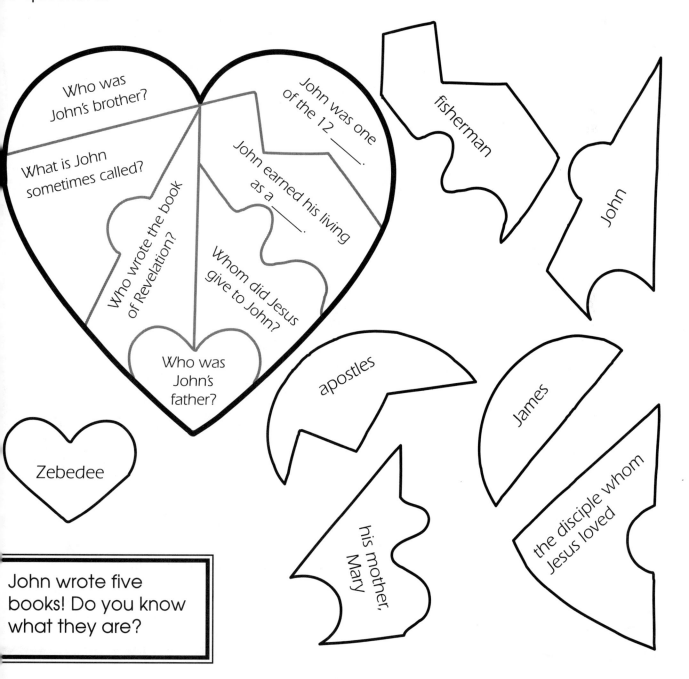

Who was John's brother?

What is John sometimes called?

Who wrote the book of Revelation?

John was one of the 12 _____.

John earned his living as a _____.

Whom did Jesus give to John?

Who was John's father?

fisherman

John

apostles

James

the disciple whom Jesus loved

his mother, Mary

Zebedee

John wrote five books! Do you know what they are?

Secret Code

(Revelation 2:10)

There was a time when people were beaten or put in prison just for being Christians! During this time, John wrote the book of Revelation. He wrote it in secret code so that Christians could read it and still be safe. John encouraged them not to give up.

The Bible verse below is written in a secret code. To find out the verse, write the next letter of the alphabet in each blank. The first two are done for you.

A B C D E F G H I J K L M N O P Q R S T U V W X Y Z

"... <u>B</u> <u>E</u> ___ A ___ ___ ___ ___ ___ ___ , even to
    A D   E   H S G E T K

the ___ ___ ___ ___ ___ ___ ___ ___ A ___ ___
    O N H M S   N E   C D   S G

and I ___ ___ ___ ___ ___ ___ ___ you the
    V H K K   F H U D

___ ___ ___ ___ ___ ___ ___ ___ ___ ___ ___ ."
B Q N V M N E K H E D

(___ ___ ___ ___ ___ ___ A ___ ___ ___ 2:10
   Q D U D K   S H N M

Angels

(Revelation 10:1; 14:6,7; 18:1; 22:8,9)

The book of Revelation tells about angels. What do angels do? Where do they live? What do they look like? Read the Bible verses listed above. Find the correct answers in the clouds and write them in the blanks. Count by 3s to connect the dots.

Angels can _____.

Angels live in _____.

Angels worship _____, but we

should _____ worship angels.

Angels are God's _____.

Angels are _____ (glowing with light).

Unit 13 . . . . Review

BUSINESS

(If there is any confusion about how to conduct class, refer to the Introduction and Unit 1 for greater detail.)

 ### Welcome

Greet the children as they come in. Use the Bible Story Club password or handshake, if they have chosen one. Congratulate the children on reaching the goals stated in the club rules. Praise their hard work and accomplishments.

 ### Attendance Charts

Give each child one sticker for attendance and one for bringing a Bible (or they can color in the squares). You may send the charts home with the children this week.

 ### Prayer Requests and Prayer

At this time, take prayer requests from the children. Honor these and then say a class prayer to begin the lesson.

LESSON

 ### Lesson Introduction

Sing one of the songs on page 73. Using the chart in the back of the book, point to each book of the New Testament as you sing. Review flash cards 1–30. Stress the ones that are most recent or any others the children are having trouble remembering. If you plan to have a program for the parents, let the children practice and rehearse at this time.

 ### Lesson

Since there is no new material, the children may enjoy playing the game described on page 67 to help them review the books of the New Testament.

Lesson continued

Using the flash cards to give you ideas, tell any New Testament story and substitute silly words for important words in the story. Have the children tell you the correct words. For example, say: When it was time for baby Jesus to be born, there was no room in the **condo**. (Children say "inn.") Mary had the baby in a stable and laid him in a **playpen**. (They say "manger.") An angel appeared to some **cowboys** watching their sheep. (They say "shepherds.") They went to worship baby **Moses**. ("Jesus")

Most children love this game and will giggle at the silly words. It helps them recall the details of the stories in a fun way. Do this with as many New Testament stories as you have time for.

Sing "The Bible Story Club" song on page 75. Give the children copies of the Bible story songs on pages 74 and 75 to take home so that they can continue to sing them in the weeks ahead. Each song will remind them of the stories they have learned. Also send a copy of the time line on pages 76 and 77 home with them.

Flash Cards

Review flash cards 1–30.

Activity Pages

Give the children copies of activity pages 68–70 to complete either in class or at home. Use page 68 to practice for the program. You can read the questions to the children as they find the answers on the time line. Or, they can do this activity in small groups, with another child reading the questions.

Assignment

Invite the parents to watch the children as they tell what they have learned about the books of the New Testament, using one of the songs on page 73, the flash cards, the charts, and the time line. Praise the children in front of their parents. Present each child with a Bible Story Club Award (page 78) at this time.

Memory Verse

I can do everything through him who gives me strength. (Philippians 4:13)

Time Line Review

Are you ready to show off everything you have learned about the New Testament? Use a copy of the time line on pages 76–77 and your own knowledge to help you find the answers to the questions below.

Which Came First . . .

1. Jesus being born or Paul becoming a missionary?

2. the church beginning or Jesus being baptized?

3. Jesus' death on the cross or Jesus going up into heaven?

4. Peter healing a lame man or John seeing a vision of heaven?

5. Jesus choosing the 12 apostles or Matthias replacing Judas?

6. Paul being put on trial or Paul being shipwrecked?

7. The New Testament or the Old Testament?

8. Peter preaching at Pentecost or Jesus going to the temple with His parents?

SS2000

My Favorite
New Testament Story

You have learned many Bible stories from the New Testament. Draw your favorite story in the Bible below.

The name of this Bible story is _____.

Bible Story Match

(Luke 2, 23, 24; Mark 4; Acts 3)

Draw a line to match the pictures for each Bible story.

SS20001

The Bible Story Club

Rules and Objectives:

1. Listen and learn when the teacher is talking.

2. Bring your Bible to class.

3. Learn to sing one of the New Testament songs.

4. Learn what each book of the New Testament is about.

5. Learn Bible stories from each book in the New Testament.

6. Find the Bible stories on the time line.

7. Learn each memory verse.

Name _____

Attendance Chart

Date	Present	Brought Bible

HOLY BIBLE

SS2000

New Testament Songs

The New Testament Song

(Tune: "Skip to My Lou")

Matthew, Mark, Luke, and John,
Tell the story of our Lord,
History of the church in Acts,
Then begin the letters.

Paul wrote to the Romans first,
Then he wrote to others, too.
1st and 2nd Corinthians,
Galatians and Ephesians.

Philippians, Colossians, and
1st and 2nd Thessalonians,
1st and 2nd Timothy,
Titus and Philemon.

Hebrews, also James,
1st and 2nd Peter, then
1st and 2nd and 3rd John,
Jude and Revelation.

From Youth Melodies and Action Songs
Copyright, 1977, Palmer Wheeler
Used by permission

Books of the New Testament

Mat - thew, Mark, Luke, and John, Acts, and the let - ter to the

Ro - mans. First and Sec - ond Cor - in - thi - ans, Ga -

la - tians, and E - phe - sians. Phil - ip - pi - ans, Co - los - sians,

First and Sec - ond Thes - sa - lon - ians, First and Sec - ond

Tim - o - thy, Ti - tus, and Phil - e - mon. He - brews, James,

First and Sec - ond Pe - ter, First and Sec - ond and

Third John, Jude, and Re - ve - la - tion.

Bible Story Songs

Unit 1: The Farmer and the Seed

(Tune: "The Farmer in the Dell")

The farmer and the seed,
The farmer and the seed,
Jesus told this parable,
The farmer and the seed.

The seed's the Word of God,
The seed's the Word of God,
The seed grows in
The hearts of men.
The seed's the Word of God.

Unit 2: Jesus Is God's Son

(Tune: "B-I-N-G-O")

I know that Jesus is God's Son
Because the Bible says so,
B-I-B-L-E, B-I-B-L-E, B-I-B-L-E,
Because the Bible says so.

I know He died upon the cross . . .

I know He lives in heaven now . . .

I know that He will come again . . .

Unit 3: The Apostles

(Tune: "Jesus Loves Me")

Jesus chose both James and John,
"Peter! Andrew! Come along,"
Philip and Bartholomew,
Doubting Thomas and Matthew.

Simon, also Thaddaeus,
James the son of Alphaeus,
Judas made the 12th one, then
Jesus was betrayed by him.

Casting lots since Judas died,
They asked God to be their guide.
So Matthias came to be
A new apostle, don't you see?

Chorus:
Yes, Jesus chose them,
Yes, Jesus chose them,
Yes, Jesus chose them,
To do good work for Him.

Unit 4: Be a Cheerful Giver

(Tune: "Skip to My Lou")

Give, give, give to the Lord,
Give, give, give to the Lord,
Give, give, give to the Lord,
Be a cheerful giver.

Unit 5: The Ephesians Song

(Tune: "Happy Birthday")

The armor of God,
The armor of God,
It says in Ephesians,
Wear the armor of God!

I will sing to the Lord,
I will sing to the Lord,
I will sing and make music
In my heart to the Lord.

Unit 6: This Is the Way We Talk to God

(Tune: "Here We Go 'Round the Mulberry Bush")

This is the way we talk to God,
Talk to God, talk to God.
This is the way we talk to God,
We bow our heads and pray.

This is the way God talks to us,
Talks to us, talks to us.
This is the way God talks to us,
We read His Word each day.

SS2000

Bible Story Songs continued

Unit 7: When I Grow Up

(Tune: "I Wish I Were an Oscar Meyer Wiener")

When I grow up, I want to be a Christian.
That is what I'd truly like to be-e-e.
When I grow up, if I become a Christian,
Jesus will be very proud of me!

Sing the song again, replacing the word Christian with what each child wants to be when he or she grows up. (Example: When I grow up, I want to be a teacher, etc.)

Unit 8: Doing Good

(Tune: "Ten Little Indians")

Doing good and helping people,
Doing good and helping people,
Doing good and helping people,
I can be like Jesus!

Unit 9: The Faith Song

(Tune: "If You're Happy and You Know It")

If you know God is real, raise your hand.
If you know God is real, raise your hand.
If you believe in Jesus, too,
Show your faith by what you do.
If you know God is real, raise your hand!

Unit 10: I Will Follow Jesus

(Tune: "Mary Had a Little Lamb")

God wants me to do what's right,
Do what's right, do what's right.
God wants me to do what's right.
I will follow Jesus.

I will follow in His steps,
In His steps, in His steps.
I will follow in His steps.
I will follow Jesus.

Unit 11: God Loves Me and God Loves You

(Tune: "Twinkle, Twinkle, Little Star")

God loves me and God loves you.
We should love each other, too.
We show love for God this way:
All His laws we will obey.
God loves me and God loves you.
We should love each other, too.

Unit 12: Revelation

(Tune: "Frère Jacques")

Revelation
Tells of heaven.
What is there?
What is there?
There will be no crying,
Sickness, pain, or dying.
God is there!
Everywhere!

Unit 13: The Bible Story Club

(Tune: "The More We Get Together")

We've learned about the Bible,
The Bible, the Bible.
We've learned about the Bible
In the Bible Story Club.
We've learned about Jesus,
And Peter and Paul.
We've learned about the Bible
In the Bible Story Club.

NEW TESTAMENT

Jesus is born.

the boy Jesus at the temple

Jesus is baptized.

Jesus chooses the 12 apostles.

A WALK DOWN BIBLE

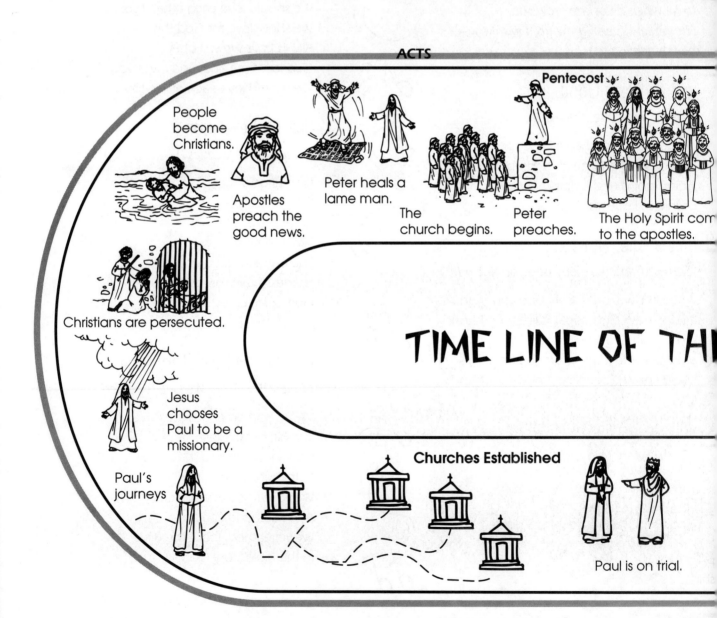

ACTS

People become Christians.

Apostles preach the good news.

Peter heals a lame man.

The church begins.

Peter preaches.

Pentecost

The Holy Spirit com to the apostles.

Christians are persecuted.

Jesus chooses Paul to be a missionary.

Paul's journeys

Churches Established

Paul is on trial.

TIME LINE OF THE

Miracles and Teachings

Jesus heals the sick.

Jesus raises the dead.

Jesus has power over nature.

Jesus tells parables.

Jesus' last week

STORY ROAD

Jesus on trial

Jesus' death

...atthias is chosen to replace Judas.

Jesus ascends into heaven.

Jesus appears to His disciples.

Jesus' burial and resurrection

NEW TESTAMENT

LETTERS
ROMANS THROUGH JUDE

REVELATION

Paul is shipwrecked.

epistles (letters) written

Paul lives in Rome.

John's vision of heaven

_____
(Member's name)

has learned all about
the New Testament
in the

Bible Story Club

Way to Go!

Signed _____

Date _____

The 12 Apostles

Peter

Andrew

James

John

Philip

Bartholomew

Thomas

Matthew

James, Son of Alphaeus

Simon

Thaddaeus

Judas

Answer Key

Page 8

Page 10

Page 13

Page 19

1. Pentecost: The church begins.
2. Peter heals a lame man.
3. Apostles preach good news.
4. People became Christians.
5. Christians are persecuted.
6. Paul's missionary journeys

Page 24

1. The child lied about breaking the TV. He should have told the truth.
2. The child did not mind her mother. She should have obeyed and made her bed.
3. The child stole some candy. He should have paid for it before he took it.

Page 33

Rejoice in the Lord always. I will say it again: Rejoice! (Philippians 4:4)

Page 43

Share your toys. Give to the needy. Visit the sick. Obey your parents. Help an elderly person. Forgive an enemy. Be a friend to someone.

Page 48

1. Jesus is better than Moses.
2. Jesus is better than the prophets.
3. Jesus is better than angels.

Page 53

1. S   2. I   3. M   4. O
5. N   Simon

Page 54

1. father   2. mother
3. teacher   4. babysitter
5. grandparents 6. police officers
7. God

Page 58

Dear friends, let us love one another, for love comes from God. (1 John 4:7)
This is how God showed his love among us: He sent his one and only son into the world . . . (1 John 4:9)
This is love for God: to obey his commands . . . (1 John 5:3)

Page 60

1. T	2. F	3. F
4. T	5. T	6. F
7. F	8. F	9. T

Page 63

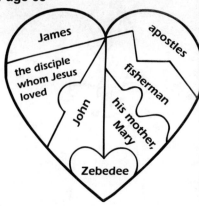

Page 64

". . . Be faithful, even to the point of death, and I will give you the crown of life." (Revelation 2:10)

Page 65

1. Angels can fly.
2. Angels live in heaven.
3. Angels worship God, but we should not worship angels.
4. Angels are God's servants.
5. Angels are radiant.

Page 68

1. Jesus being born
2. Jesus being baptized
3. Jesus' death on the cross
4. Peter healing a lame man
5. Jesus choosing the 12 apostles
6. Paul being put on trial
7. the Old Testament
8. Jesus going to the temple with His parents

Page 70

SS2000